"A small company with untold potential"

Giglets Ltd.

"Oor Rabbie"

For Scotland's Children
To learn, enjoy
and cherish
The world of Robert Burns

Tam O'Haggis

Giglets Ltd.

Written by Louise Bennett and Fiona Morton
Ilustrated by Tom Brodie-Browne and Kayleigh Wright

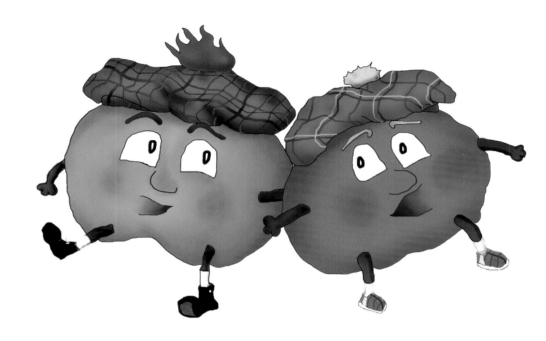

Tam O'Haggis staggered out,
While Johnny Souter fell about.

Tam looked round to find his mare,
Her name is Meg, she's over there.

The clock, it showed that it was late,
Sat by the fire, his dear wife Kate.
Gathering her brow like the gathering storm,
Nursing her wrath to keep it warm.

Into the storm they rode so fast,
Hoping the rain, it would not last.
Whilst holding tight his good green bonnet,
While singing over an old Scots sonnet.

The lightning flashed from pole to pole,
Near and more near the thunders roll.

As he longed for his safe bed,
Kirk Alloway appeared up ahead.

Something there did not seem right,
There was dance and music in the night.
The windows seemed to glow like fire,
As owls circled round the spire.

They ventured forward to the light,
Where Tam saw such an awful sight.
The Devil's bagpipes filled with sound,
As all the witches danced around.

Hornpipes, jigs, strathspeys and reels,
Put life and rhythm in their heels.
The piper loud and louder blew,
The dancers quick and quicker flew.

Tam watched one witch, fell in a trance,
Enchanted by her magical dance.
And roared out "Weel Done, Cutty-Sark!"
And in an instant all was dark.

As Tam and Meg turned round to run,
The witches' chase had just begun.
Tam knew the witches were at a loss,
For running water they dare not
cross.

One witch was faster than her team,
And was getting closer to the stream
They made it through the wind and hai
But not before Meg lost her tail.

If going out you are inclined,
And Cutty-Sark runs in your mind.